FUTZIE NUTZLE'S

Modern Loafer

Thames and Hudson

Library of Congress Catalog Card Number: 81-50522
ISBN: 0-500-27231-X

Printed in the U.S.A. by Command Litho
Designed by Janet Doyle

1 2 3 4 5 6 7 8 9 0

Introduction

One day while at a combination picnic and softball game in Santa Cruz, California, I was loitering on the outskirts of some girls in shorts who kept bending over to pick up badly thrown frisbees, when I was approached by an individual nearly six feet tall, who introduced himself as Futzie Nutzle, a man whose origins are shrouded in mystery.

So much for Nutzle the man: Nutzle the artist produces works of surgical precision, like lenses which allow us to peek at his neurons and synapses, and since his pictures speak so clearly for themselves I am left with not much to say, so here is a true story:

I live in an apartment by the water, and one night a friend and I were sitting around when we heard a great commotion just offshore. It was the awful quacking and splashing sound of a duck being eaten by something. Picturing in my mind the great white shark, Godzilla, or a school of hungry cartoonists, I ran up to the car to get my long range $18.00 police special flashlight, thinking that somehow we could help the duck when we could see what was eating it. By the time I returned, the duck was periodically being pulled under, so I aimed and clicked on the positive two-position switch. All that happened was a dismal and irritating flicker. Reasoning calmly, I banged and smashed the light on the deck railing, but no amount of maintenance would produce anything stronger than a cigarettelike glow, except for an occasional flash of brightness when it was not pointed at the now terminally eaten duck. The duck was gone, the eater was gone, and I was left with a piece of useless black-anodized aluminum, which, though worth $18.00 (not including three new batteries), I flung into the Bay. The second it left my hand it lit up with a brilliance that would have made its mother proud and sank into about five feet of water, shining for all it was worth. The last time I looked, at one in the morning, the light was still lit. The next day it disappeared into San Francisco Bay.

Good luck Nutty.

B. Kliban

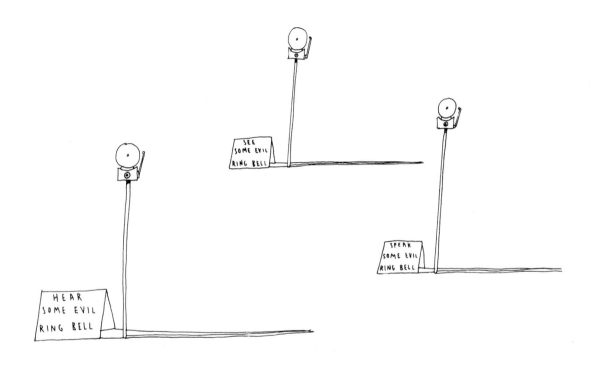

HELLS BELLS

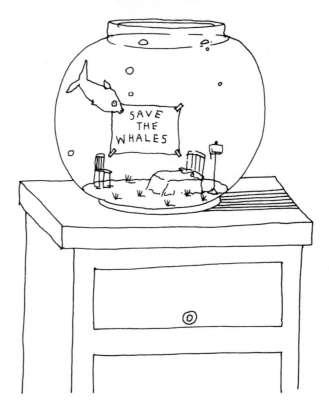

FIRE QUACKER.

JUST
ABOUT
RIGHT

HOTTER THAN
HELL

COLDER THAN
SHIT

OUR SOLAR
SYSTEM.

Nutzly

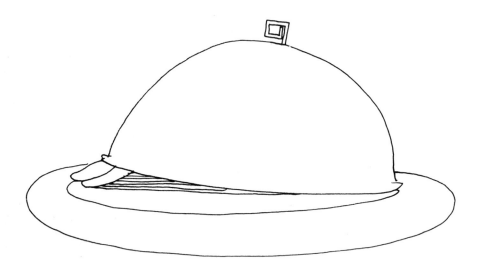

PEEKING DUCK.

LOOKING FOR WORK.

WHAT STARS DO DURING
THE DAY.

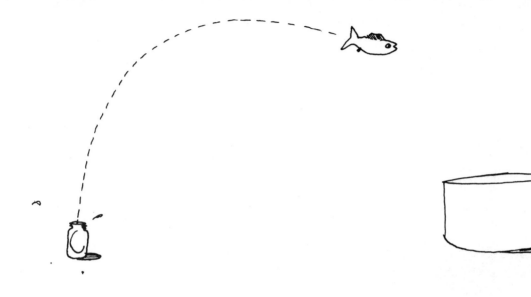

PROGRESS.

Nutzly

GETTING TO THE
POINT.

Nukler

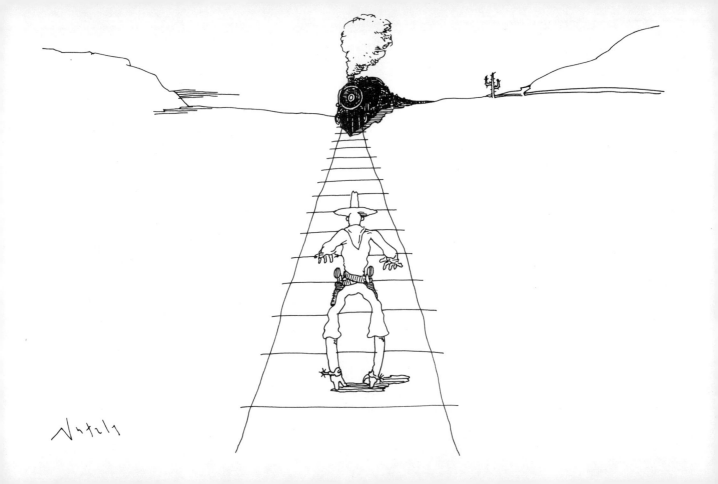

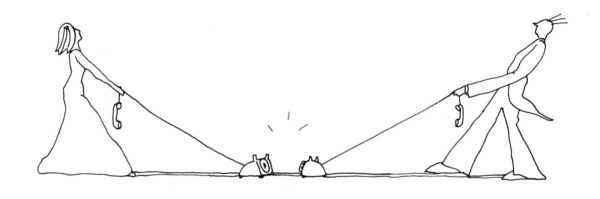

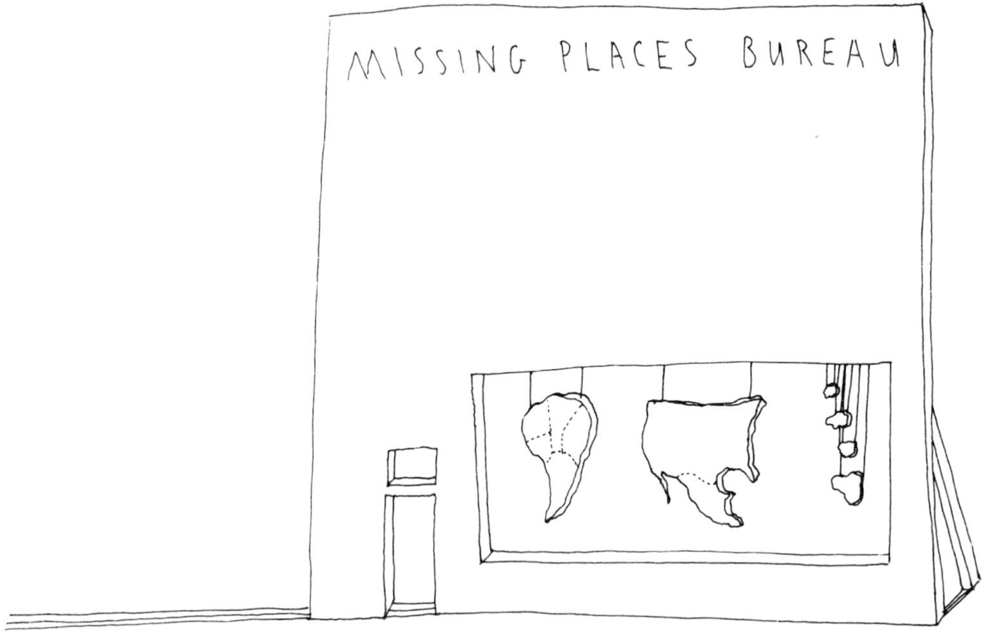
MISSING PLACES BUREAU

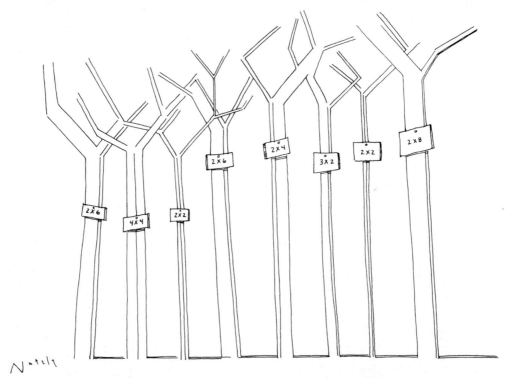

PRE CUT WOODS.

Somewhere along the line.

Natel

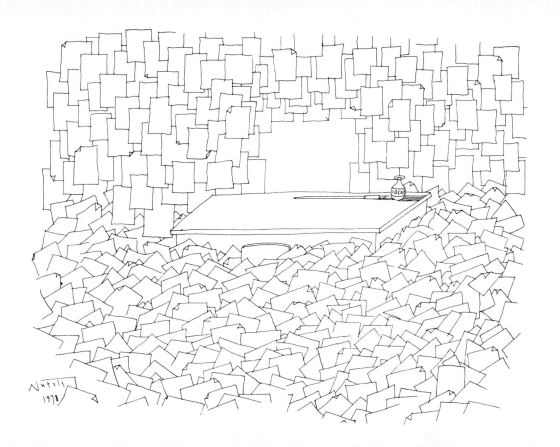

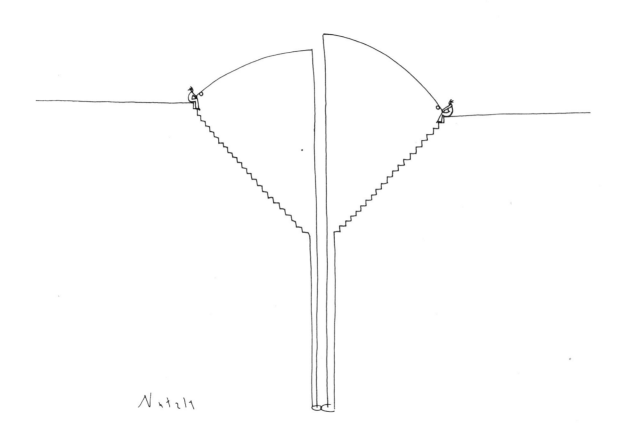

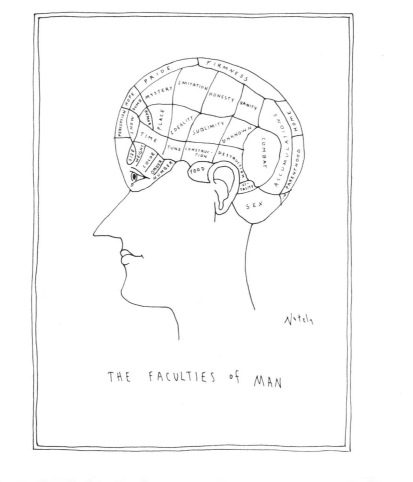

THE FACULTIES OF MAN

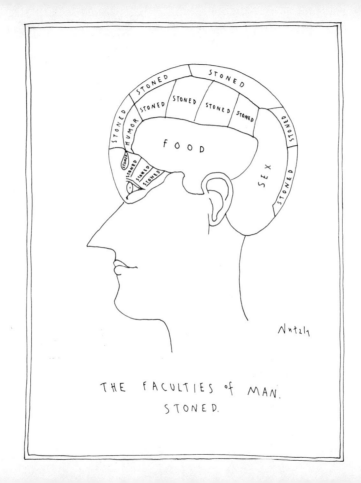

THE FACULTIES of MAN.
STONED.

Body Building

Heyday! Heyday!

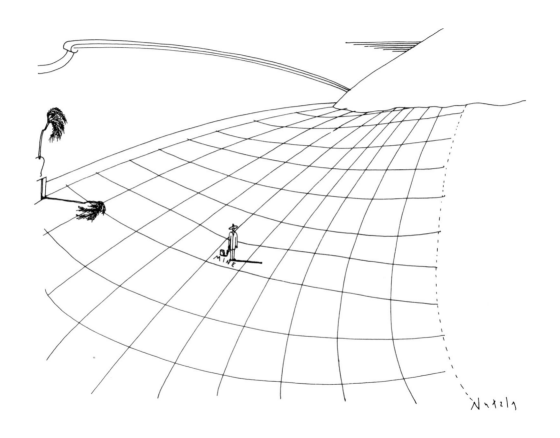

MINE

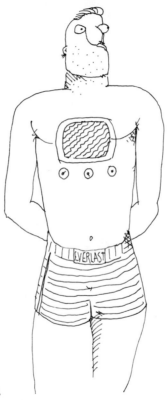

Nutela

TV REPAIR

IT'S NOT YOUR SET.

BATTLE OF BRAINS.

TV STORY

CHANNEL 2, HOSPITAL POLICE
CHANNEL 3, EMERGENCY CLINIC
CHANNEL 4, POLICE DOCTOR
CHANNEL 5, NEWS, FEATURING HOSPITAL DIVORCE
CHANNEL 6, ACADEMY WINNING DOCTOR
CHANNEL 7, RESCUE POLICE (R)
CHANNEL 8, POLICE ACADEMY AWARDS
CHANNEL 9, HOSPITAL SURGERY
CHANNEL 10, POLICE EMERGENCY
CHANNEL 11, SURGERY ACADEMY AWARDS (R)
CHANNEL 12, HOSPITAL ZONE
CHANNEL 13, I'M GETTING SNOW ON CHANNEL 13.

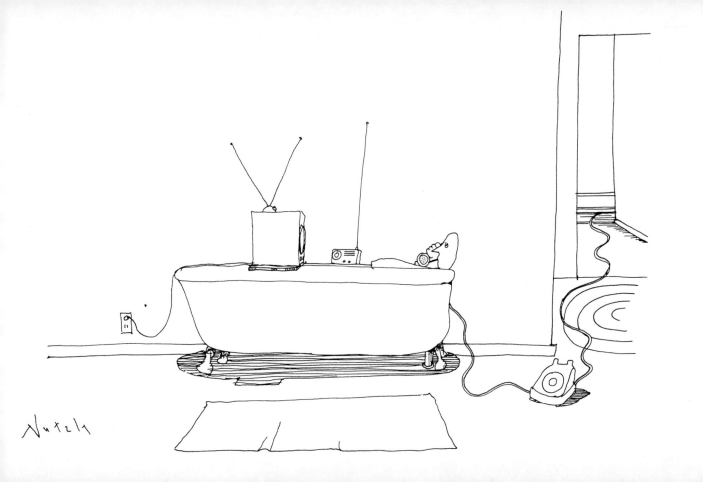

NEWS ANCHORMEN

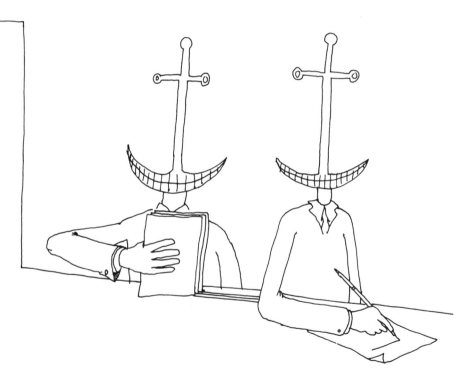

Nutzli

RENEWED AMERICAN SPIRIT,

How to keep your eggs.

FLU BAIT.

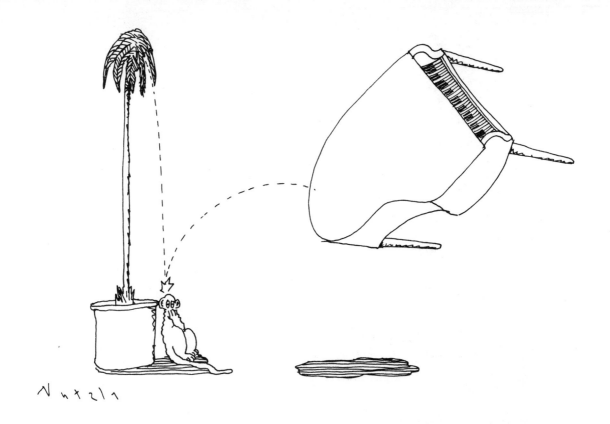

Nutch

Moo Moo in Moo Moo.

Nutela

Boxcanyon

OLD FISH HOME.

Nutzli

PILES OF SMILES.

POTENTIALLY, EACH DAY IS CRUCIAL IN
THE TOTAL DEVELOPMENT.

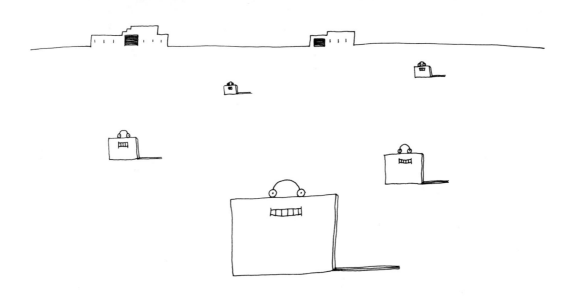

NUTCASES.

Natela

Nutzli

Toilet training

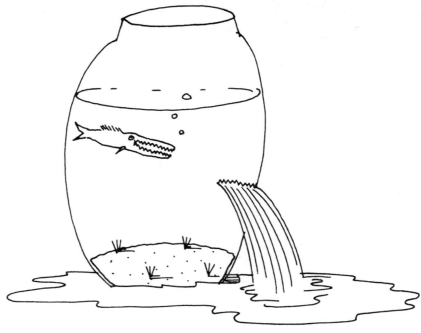

10 FT. POLE

NUCLEAR
POWER

PERFUMANCE ON RODEO DRIVE.

MEMORIAL MORNING

DIFFERENT BRANDS OF HUMOR.

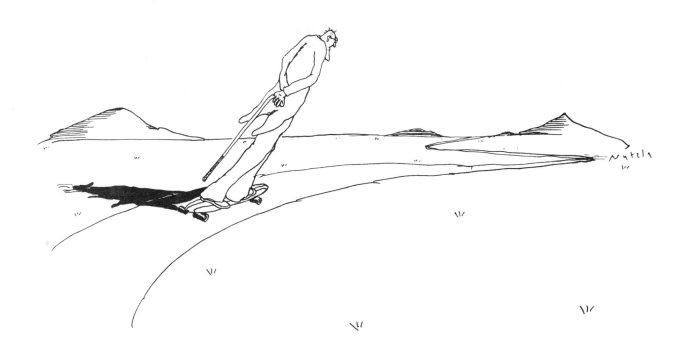

Wiseacre.

A LIGHT IN THE FOREST.

THE SIMPLE LIFE.

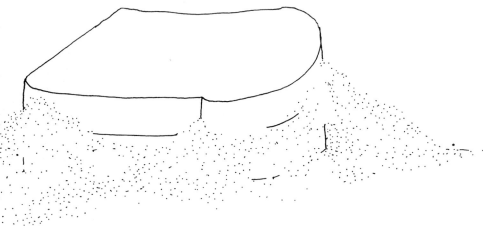

Sandwich.

Nutela

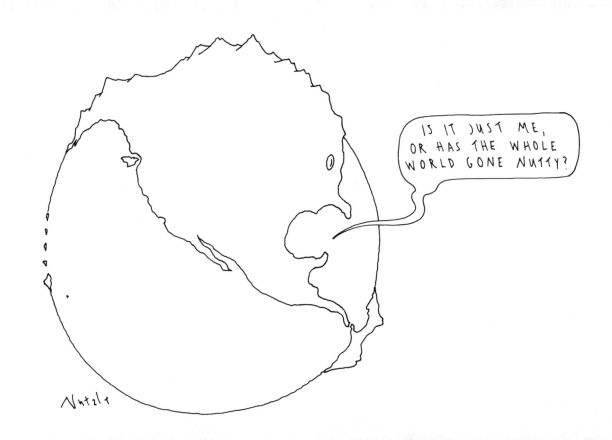

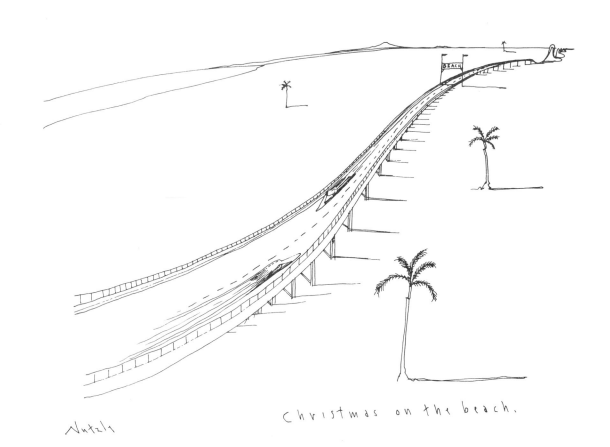

Nutzli

christmas on the beach.

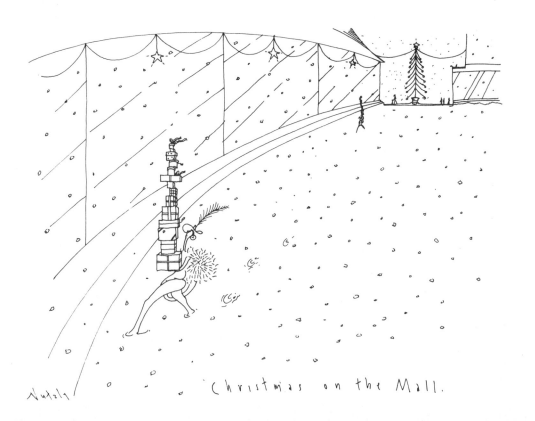

Christmas on the Mall.

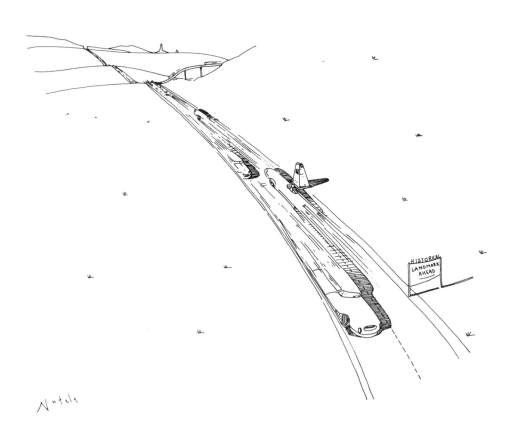

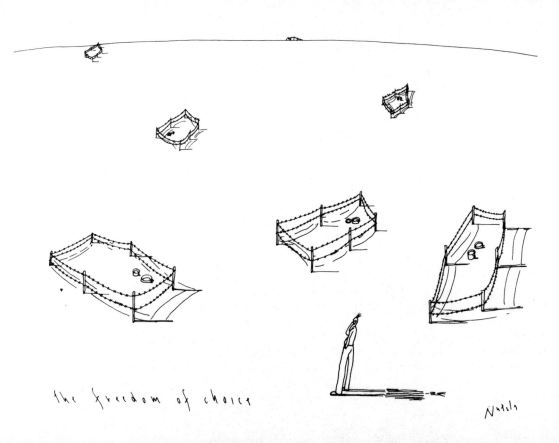

the freedom of choice

Nutila

ANNUAL MEETING OF THE EGG ADVISORY BOARD.

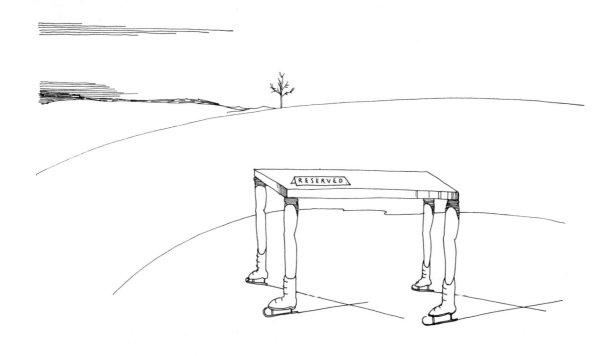

RESERVED

TAKE A CHANCE.

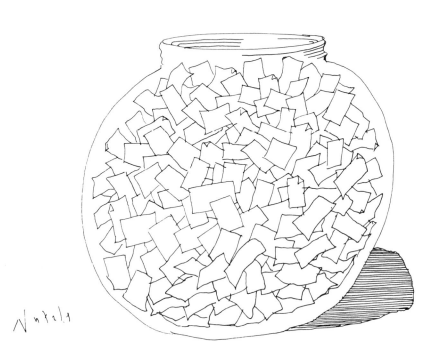

Breaking the Ice.

Natela

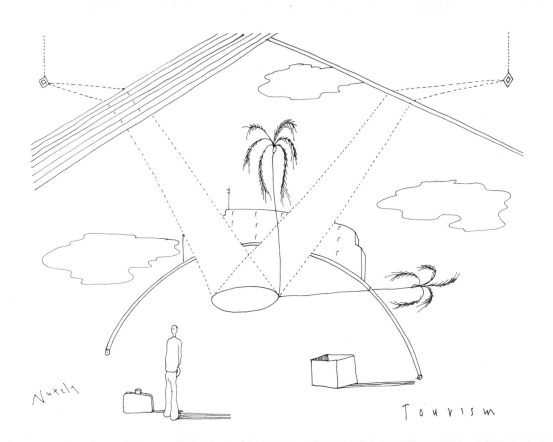

Tourism

AIR MAIL SPECIAL DELIVERY,

CARPENTERS' HOUSE

LEARNING THE ROPES.

THE WORKS.

PUSHING IT TO THE EDGE.

READERSHIP

Natila

ADVERB & ADJECTIVE INC.

Nutch

Publishing House

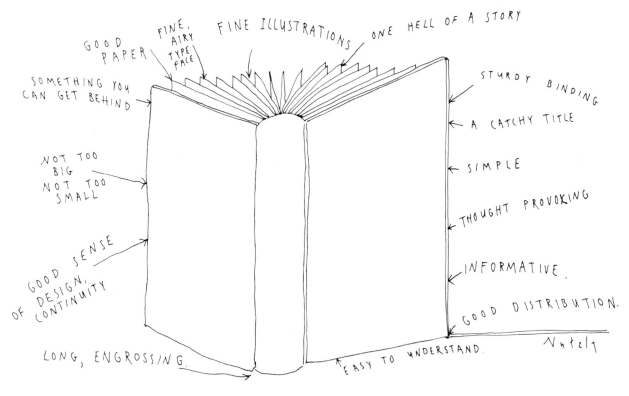

GOOD PAPER

FINE, AIRY TYPE FACE

FINE ILLUSTRATIONS

ONE HELL OF A STORY

SOMETHING YOU CAN GET BEHIND

STURDY BINDING

A CATCHY TITLE

NOT TOO BIG NOT TOO SMALL

SIMPLE

THOUGHT PROVOKING

GOOD SENSE OF DESIGN, CONTINUITY

INFORMATIVE.

GOOD DISTRIBUTION.

Nutzl7

LONG, ENGROSSING.

EASY TO UNDERSTAND.

SIGNS OF A GOOD BOOK.

A BOOK THAT REALLY GRABS A PERSON.

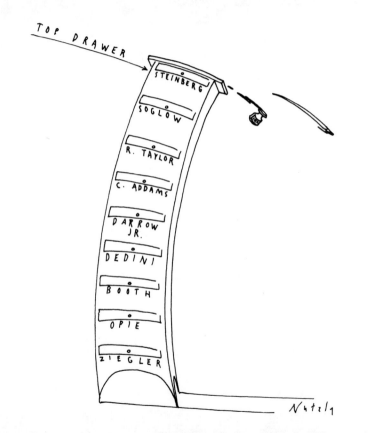

NEW ARRIVALS

SEND THESE OUT

SAME OLD BULLSHIT

THE CARTOONISTS DESK.

Hawaiian Perplexity.

How to draw
a reject.

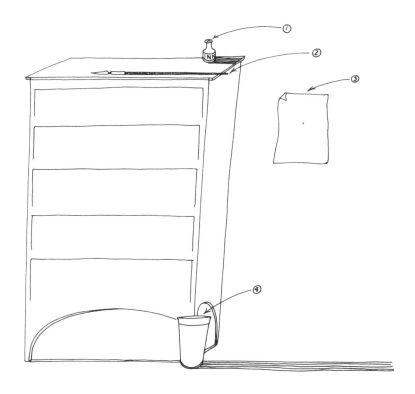

① ② ③ ④

Nutal 1978.

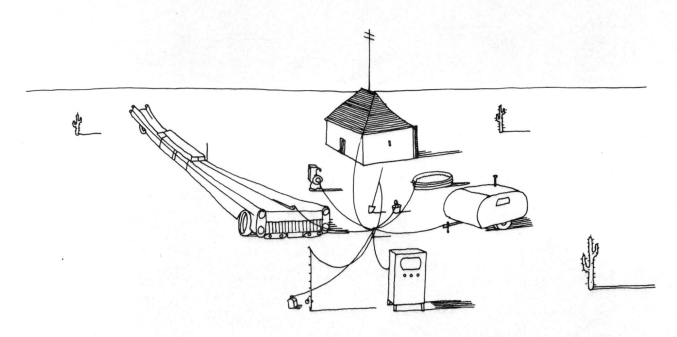

EVERYTHING AT STAKE.

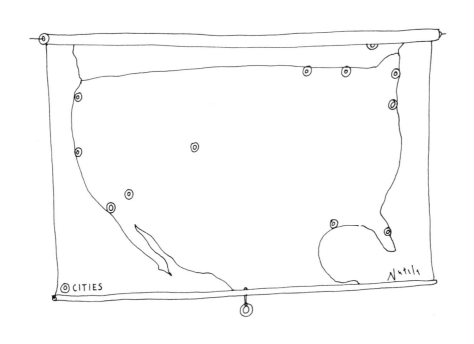

◎ CITIES

Natila

CHEAP MAP

Frank and Earnest.

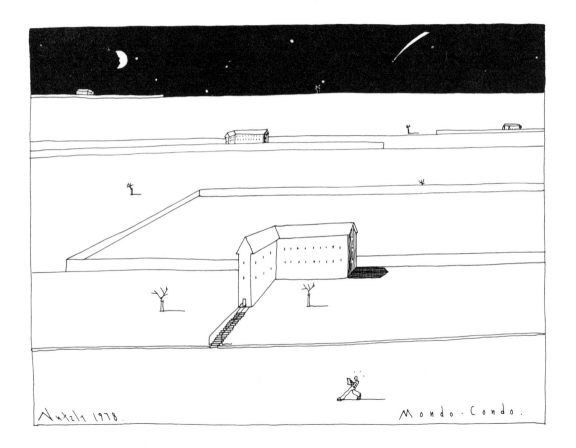

Nutch 1978.

Mondo - Condo.

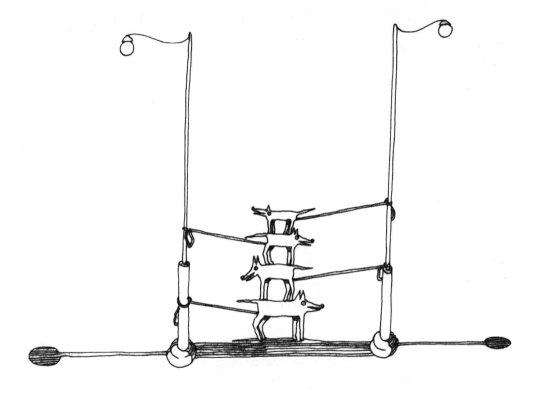

Nutili

Civic pride

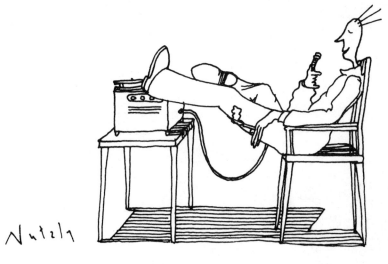

IDEAL INTERVIEW.

Nutels

SHELL FACTORY

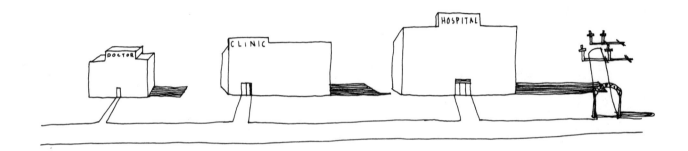

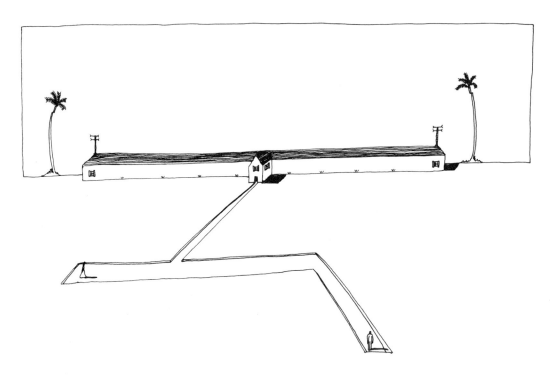

RICH SPAT

Natels

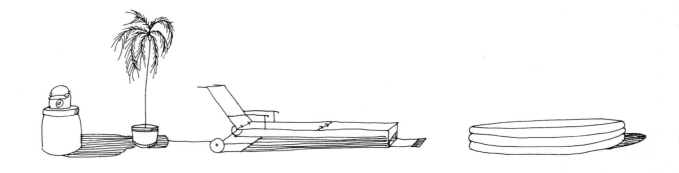

N u l c l n

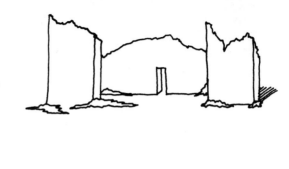

And That's That.

Nutzly

THAT OLD RIVER KEEPS CALLING MY NAME.

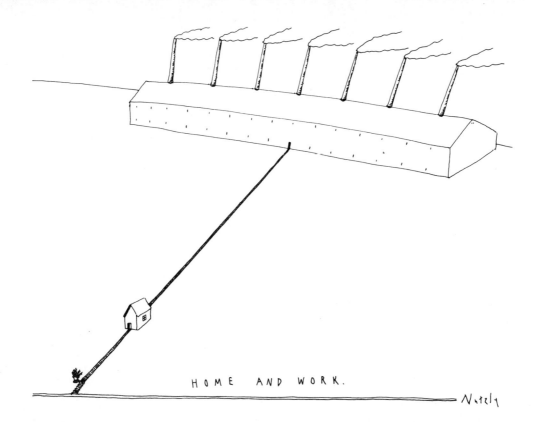

HOME AND WORK.

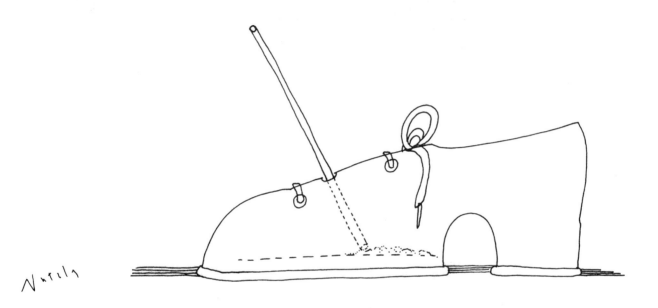

— S N O W S H O E —

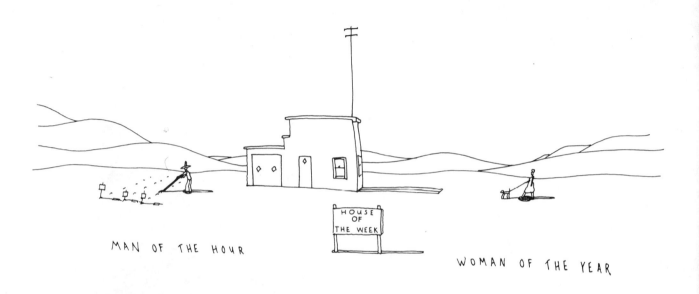

MAN OF THE HOUR

HOUSE
OF
THE WEEK

WOMAN OF THE YEAR

Nutzl

LANDMARKS

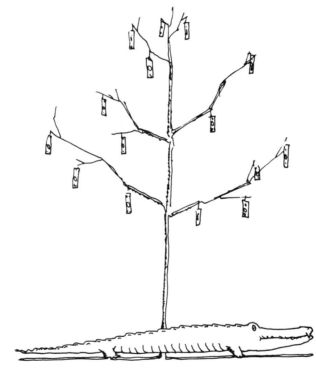

Nutela

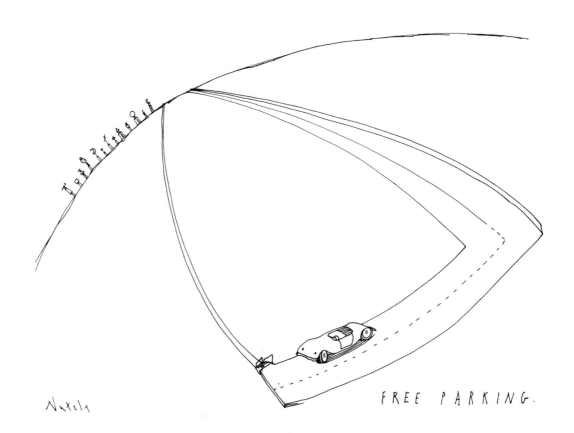

Natila

FREE PARKING.

THE FILTHY RICH:..

Nutale

MISSLE BEACH

SELF PORTRAIT

GAS O' LINE.

ESCAPE ARTIST.

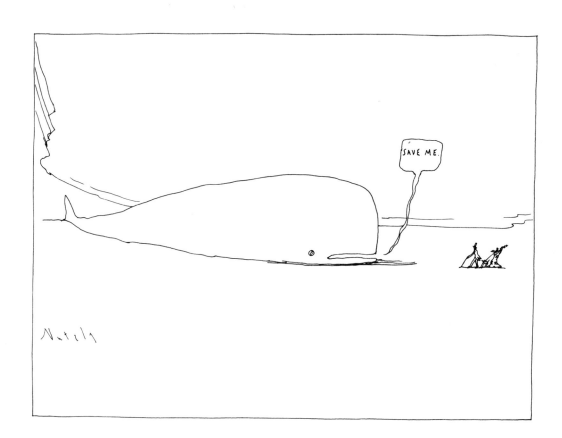